# NATIONAL LAMPOON PRESENTS

# Claire BRETÉCHER

Translated and edited by Valerie Marchant
Lettered and art directed by John Workman
Copy edited by Susan Devins

# INTRODUCTION

The idea for "Les Frustrés" came to me one day when I was thinking about these inexpressible contradictions, all the little things, some of them embarrassing, that you have in your head. For instance, once I drew a woman who couldn't decide whether she wanted a child. She hesitates, takes the Pill, then stops, thinks about her career, then about how sad it is to grow old without children. She finally concludes that the ideal would be to get pregnant without doing it on purpose. At one point in my life, I thought just like her. Women understand my cartoons much better than men do. I don't mind giving feminists a hard time, probably because I'm squarely on their side.

People often recognize themselves in my drawings—or at least they think they do. Every time I call a character "Gisèle," three Gisèles call me to say I'm exaggerating.

Women in comic strips are usually portrayed either as shrews or as movie stars. But in real life, women, like men, are neither of these extremes, so I portray women and men alike, except that the women have two little round things on their chest.

I hate to work. When I sit down at my desk on Tuesday at 10 A.M. to finish my page by 5 P.M., I never know what I'm going to do. Sometimes I overhear a conversation and then use it word for word. Last week I heard a young woman giving advice to another woman who was job-hunting. "Do what I did, sign up for a Spanish course so you can get a job as a maid." Usually I get ideas from letters to the editor, from friends, most from my own life. Every time I finish a page, I'm convinced it's the last one I'll ever do.

*Claire*
*BRETÉCHER*

From "Claire Bretécher's Comedie Française," *Ms. Magazine*, March 1978.

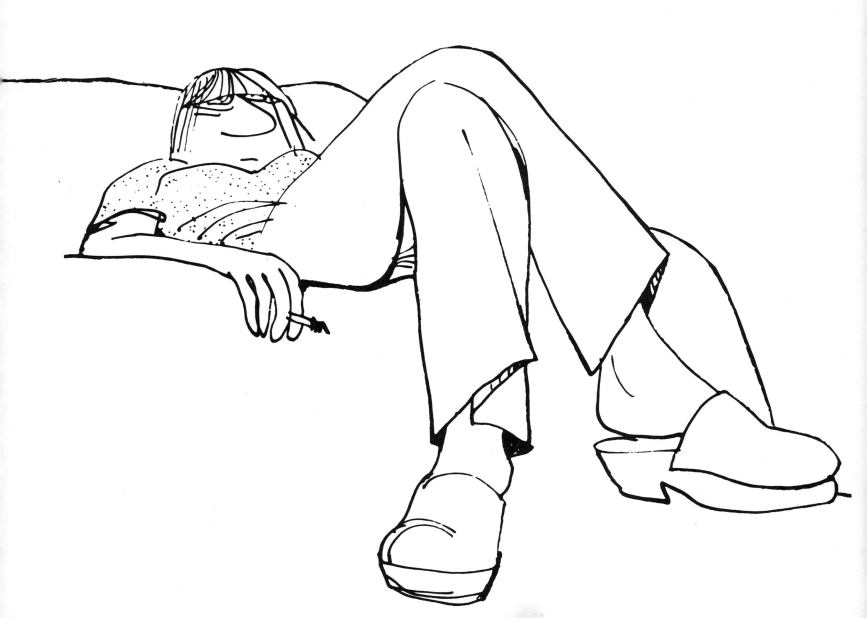

# LADIES AND GENTLEMEN

# RAISING DEMONS

# THE PURISTS

BRETÉCHER

# our lady of mercy

# THE JOYS OF FREELANCE

# best laid plans

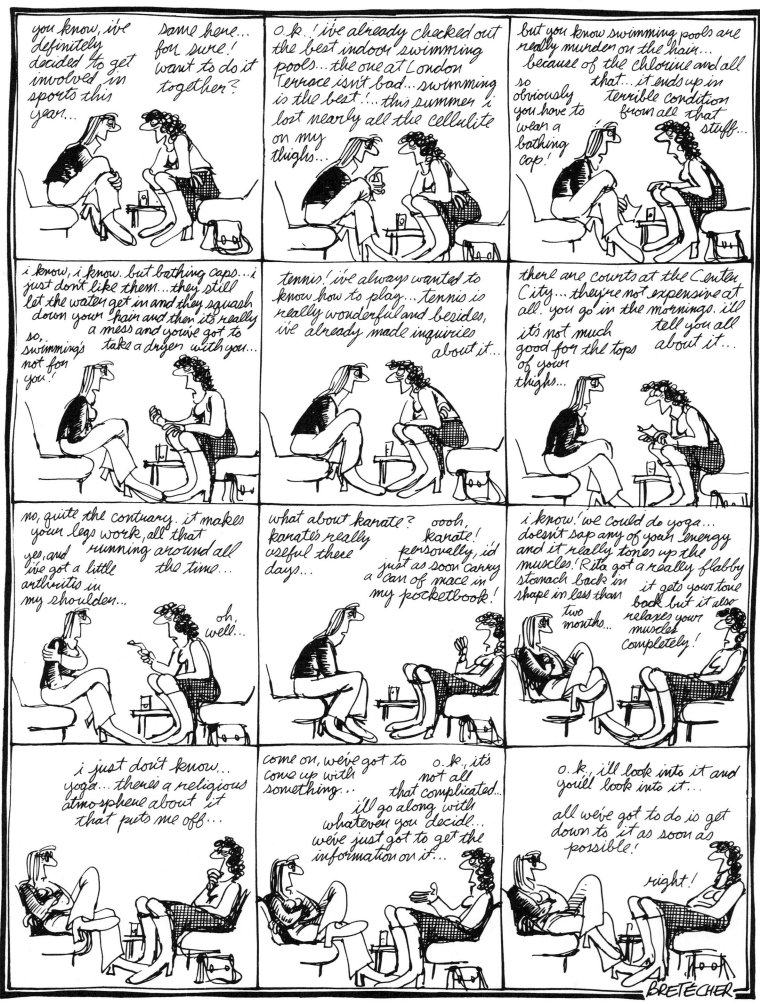

# MOOD MUSIC

— and so forth.....

BRETÉCHER

# THE CHURCH IN OUR TIME

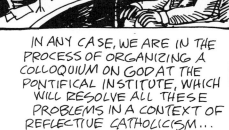

# TRUE CONFESSIONS

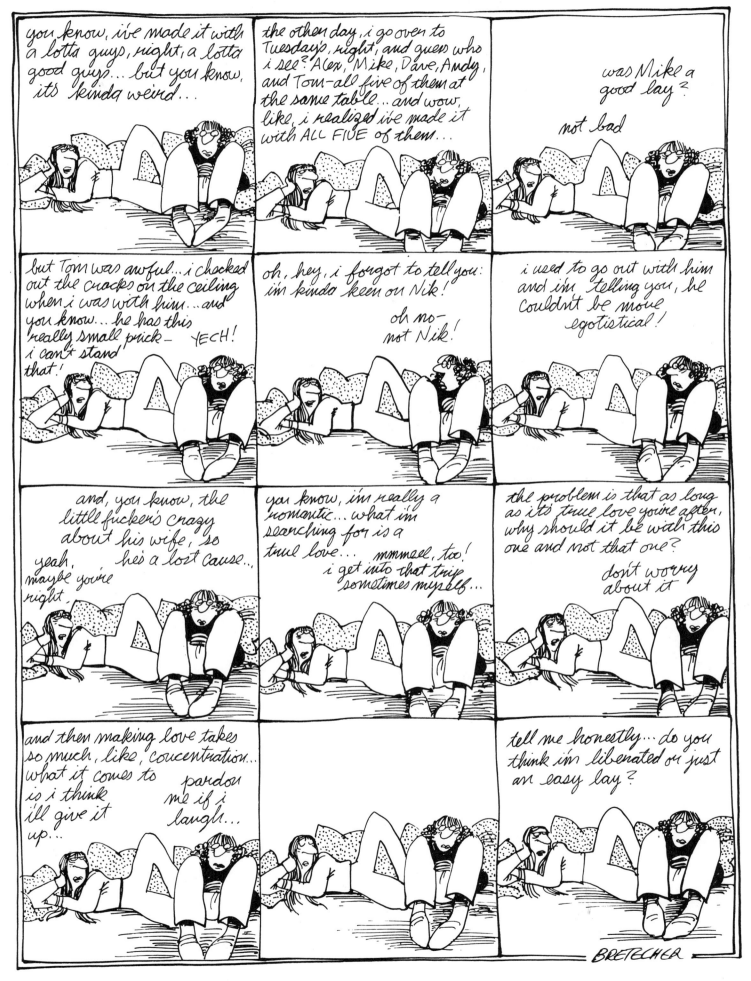

# MADNESS

# QUOTATIONS FROM THE CHAIRMAN

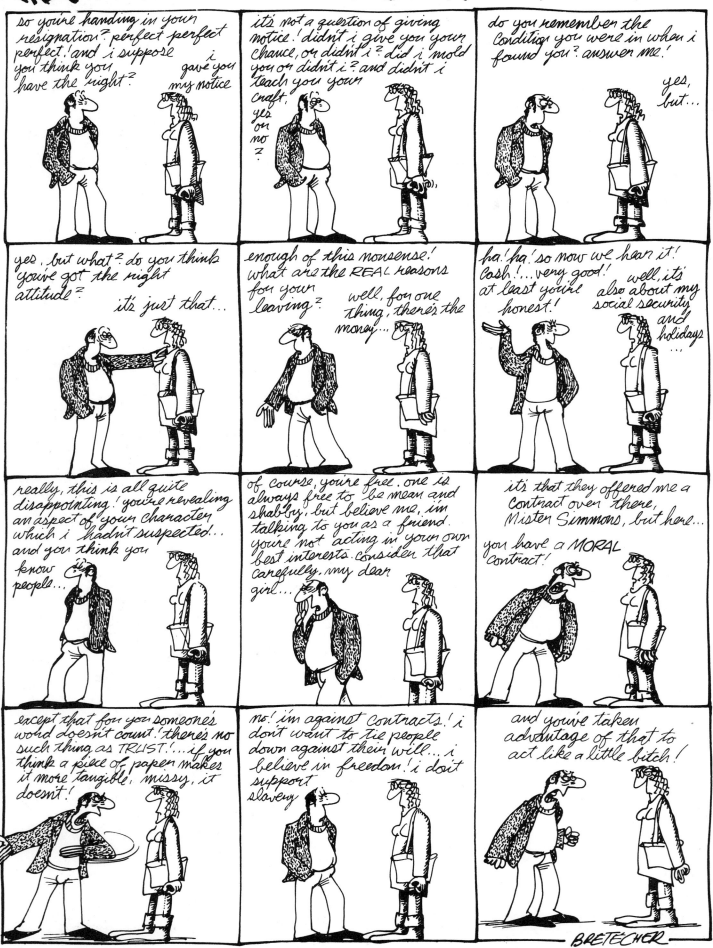

# COMPARATIVE RELIGION

# DOWN AND OUT

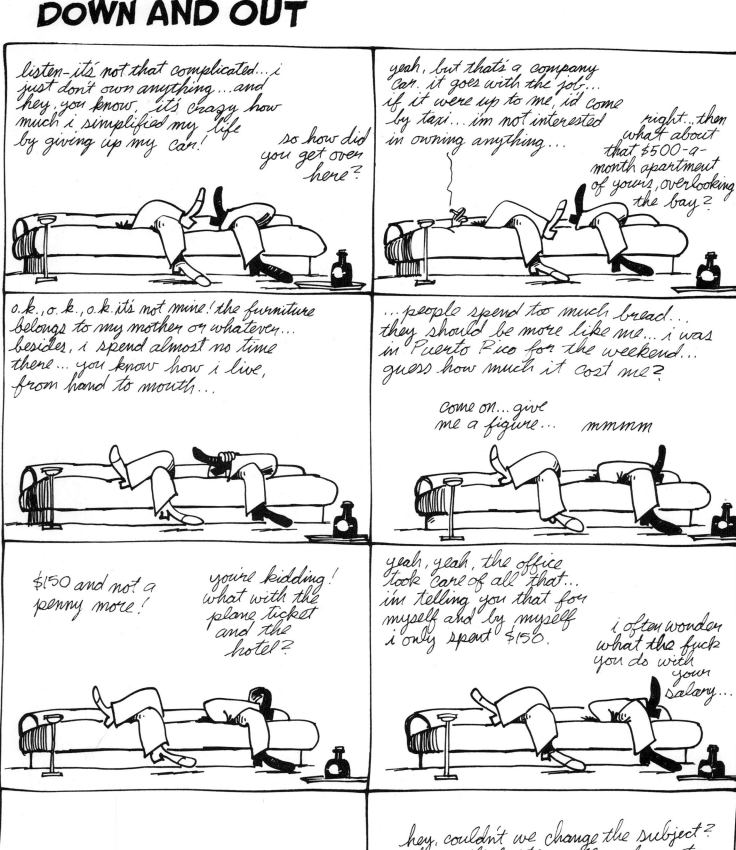

BRETÉCHER

# BEASTLY FRIENDS

# THE MATERNAL INSTINCT

# DOWN TIME

so, Mike, what've you got to say for yourself? say, you gotta tan? *yeah, i was on the coast*

a creative seminar paid for by the office... but really something... a kind of Esalen thing, super-luxurious, very, very nice... *just what did this seminar consist of?*

on the first day you learn to concentrate and deconcentrate, by breathing, you know...

after that you go eat, then there are discussions on creativity, but very free, no direction to speak of... you're in separate cabins with earphones... after meals, you relax...

on the second day, someone projects colors on a television screen... when one of them reminds you of something, you press on a button...

for example, if you're reminded of a bird, you push button "b"... that initiates another series of images, and soon... after that you eat... and, believe me, very well indeed

there are some little bits, you know, shticks... there are round tables with well-known artists... very likable

they explain where they get their ideas, and all that. you eat with them, relax together...

mind you, you don't work hard all day long... there's plenty of free time... there's a discothèque, a movie theater, an auditorium... bloody terrific, really...

it's situated on very nice grounds with a swimming pool, saunas, you eat well, there's horses... the hostesses aren't half bad...

it costs the office a piss-pot of money, but if it manages to inspire the public relations department of Mobil Oil, then i'm all for it...

anyway, that's not my problem... right now i've just got one thing on my mind: my holidays...

BRETÉCHER

# A MAN OF PRINCIPLE

# DEPRIVED CHILDHOOD

Susan was invited for a weekend in the country with a friend from school.

...and let me tell you: this girl is Klein the designer's kid... there's tennis courts and a swimming pool--you know the type!

...so i said to her: "listen, you have to understand that there are people who have a lot of money, and that's not what's important...

...we don't have that much, but that's not the thing... i mean, that's not what matters."

you have to understand that not everyone can have a tennis court--sometimes the yard's too small, so you can very well go to the club like everyone else

so i said to her: "listen, so we don't have three cars, so when mummy needs the Mercedes, you can easily take a taxi with Stella... or even, hey, a bus, if it comes to that!

"you ought to realize you're lucky to have a housekeeper to take care of you... when i was your age at Zayda and Bubbe's, there was only one maid...

so, little Miss Lesser, you can just quit it with the martyr number already..."

i explained to her very nicely that there's no way to have a swimming pool here! it's nice enough to have one when we go to Florida.... well i might as well have saved my breath!

i can't stand for my daughter to have an elitist attitude!! it's really the limit when you consider the ideas her father and i have!

there are times when i tell myself it would have been better to send her to the public school around the corner! that would have taught her a lesson!

the problem is that it really isn't practical for her to go to the public school--they finish classes on Friday at such an outlandish hour!

BRETECHER

# A FAIRY STORY

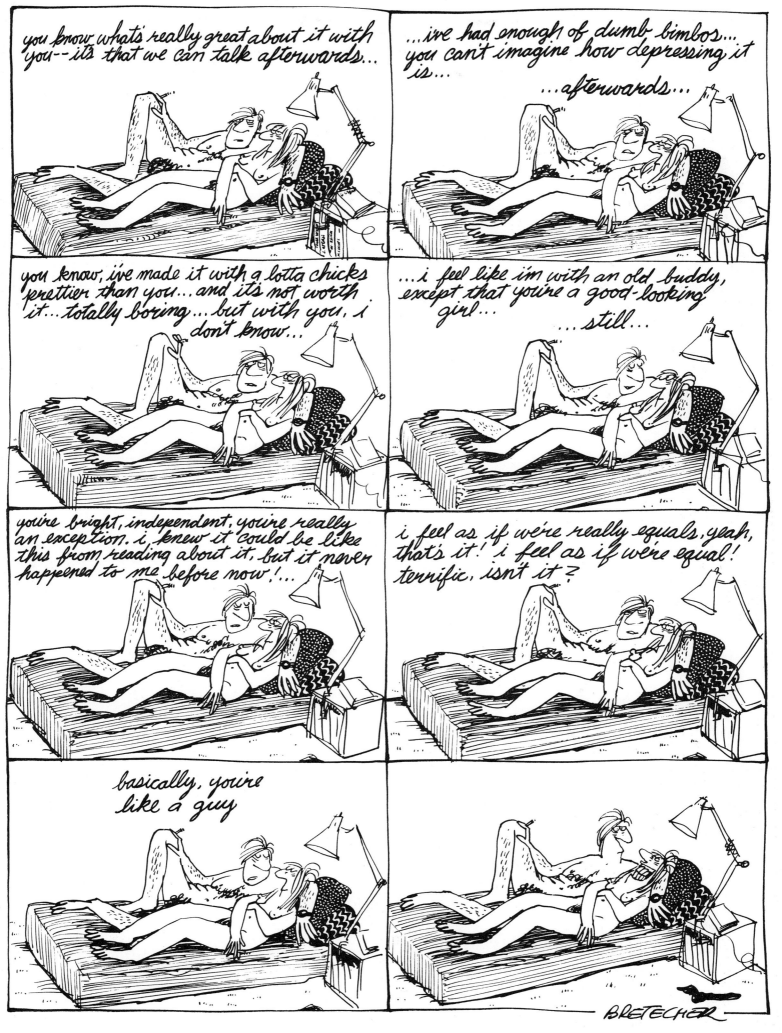

# "STEREO"

# BETHLEHEM '78

# PASSION

# ON THE BEACH

BRETECHER

# i FEEL PRETTY

# HELP

# SECOND THOUGHTS

# The NEUROTIC Child

# MOVING PICTURES

# MEANINGFUL DIALOGUE

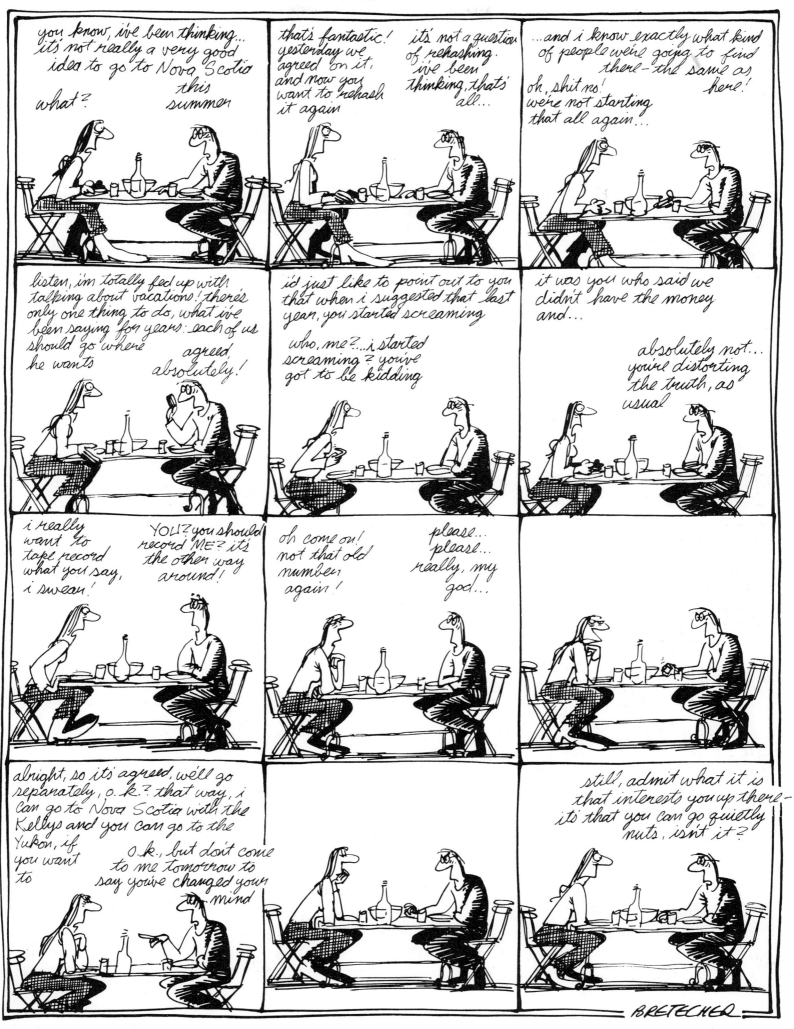

# FANTASY SEQUENCE

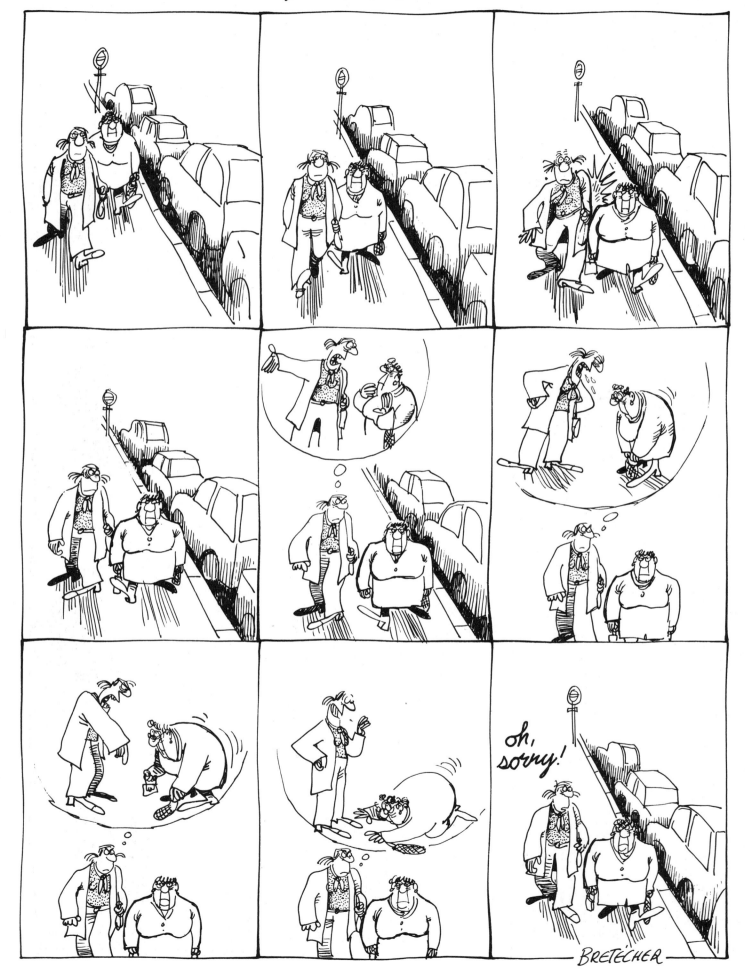

# THE CREATIVE WOMAN

# CELLULITE

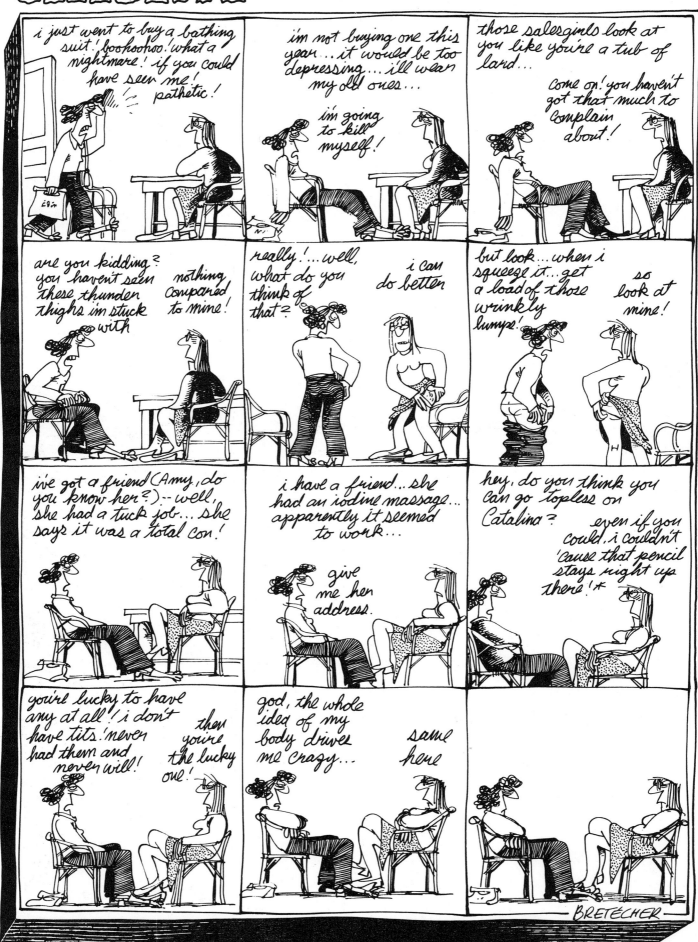

A PENCIL TEST: PLACE A PENCIL HORIZONTALLY UNDER THE BREAST. IF IT STAYS THERE, TOO BAD.
(FOR THE UNINITIATED)

# RUMINATIONS

# NOSTALGIA

# IDENTITY CRISIS

it just kills me to be trapped inside my body... i'd really like to escape from it! it's a drag!

i know exactly what you mean

for example, i'd like to know what it would be like to be a woman... you know, i'd like to be in your place...

you wouldn't believe what it's like...

i just can't stand myself! can't even look at myself anymore in the mirror! i want just one thing: to be someone else.

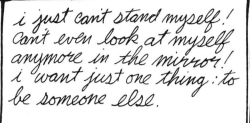

really, it's ghastly to be only oneself, don't you think? it's so limiting... hey, i'd like to be John Phillips - he has a really far-out life - like a sort of Hindu holy man...

yeah... i'd like to be Carol Boswell... i can really see myself as Carol Boswell... or maybe a farmer...

yeah, not bad... i'd like to be Picasso. no, that's impossible now - he's dead.

who would you like to change places with?

no one... i'm just fine the way i am...

then i want to be in your place!

BRETECHER

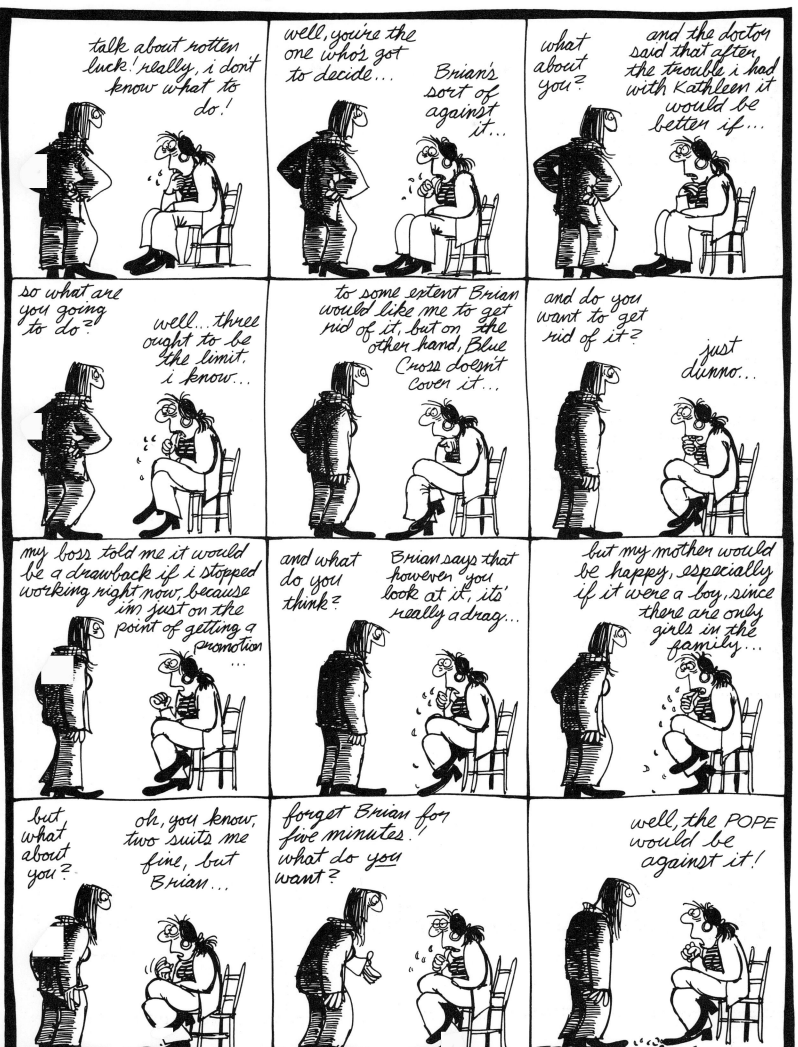

# DIES IRAE

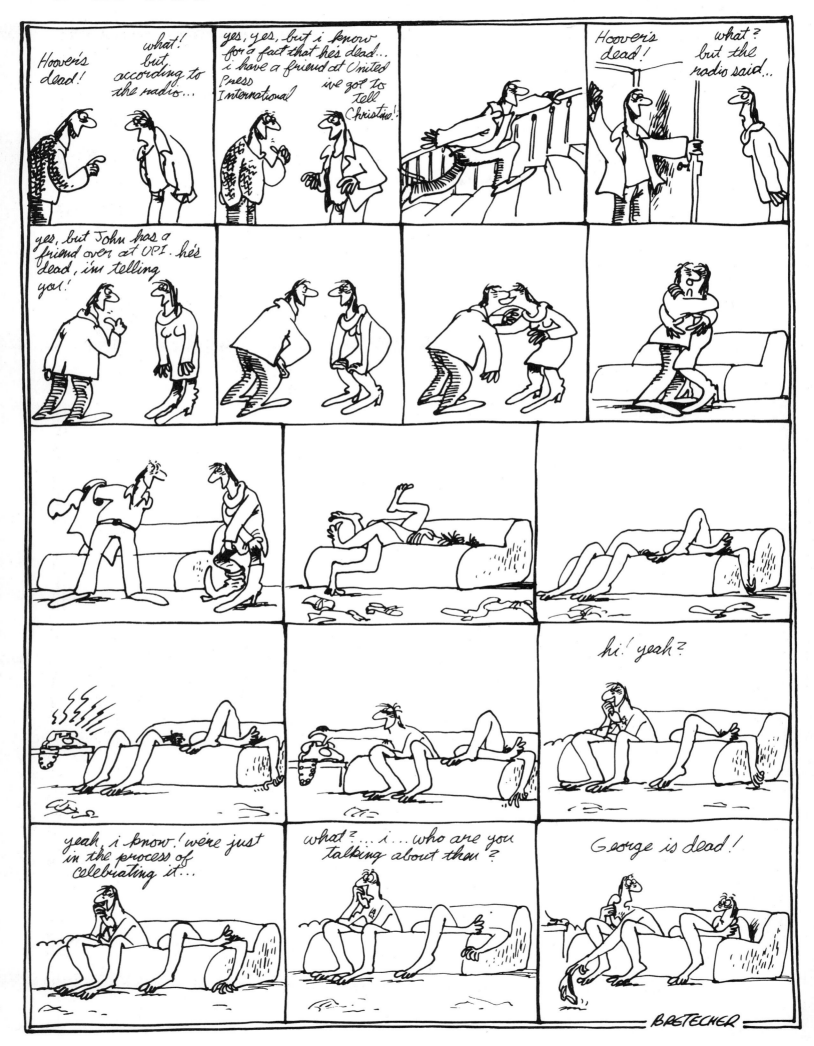

BRETECHER

# A MAN AND A WOMAN

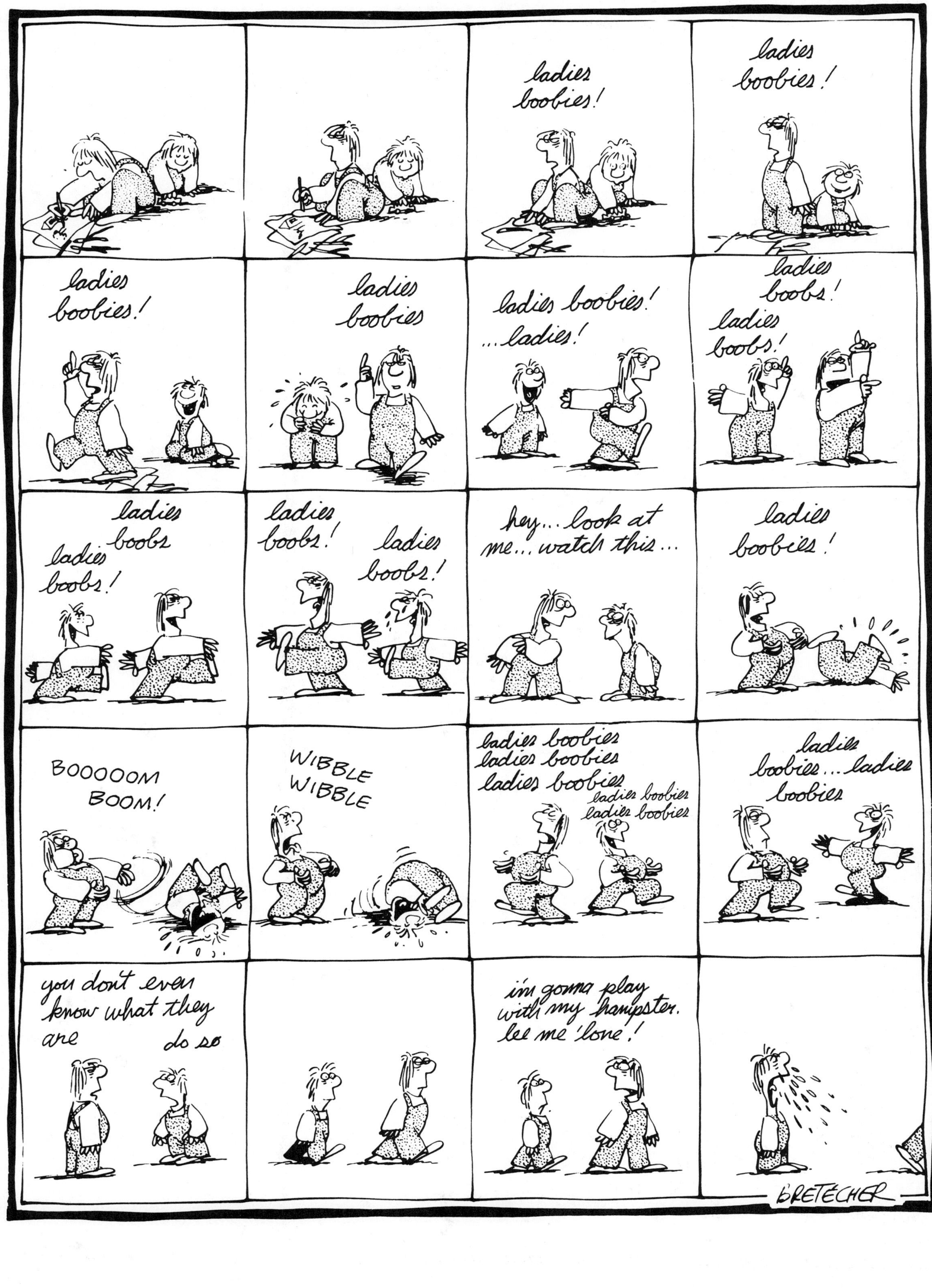

# CRITICS

that was terrible! no sense of subtlety! no social awareness... there was no connection between the style of the direction and the script...

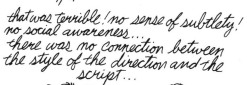

nothing was internalized... even worse, it was politically unsound... here we are again with the worst kind of slapstick!

typical Broadway play!

so true!

BRETÉCHER

# THUNDER THIGHS

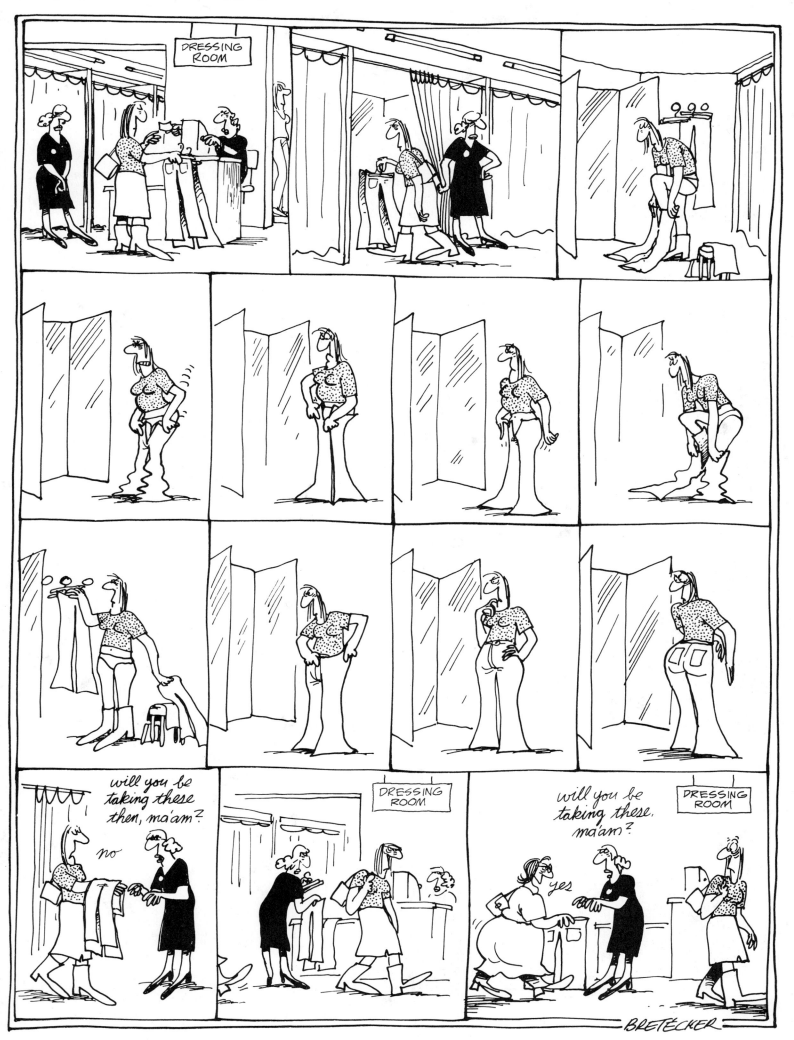

# A SIMPLE MAN

at Easter, when we were staying in a house in Virginia that belongs to Julia's mother, i talked to the gardener for an hour or so...
an incredible man-he and i could really communicate...
...he certainly wasn't a cultured person, and he only had a vocabulary of about two thousand words...
still, i didn't have any trouble communicating with him... it was a kind of encounter...
obviously, i talked to him about things that interested him: lettuce, tomatoes...
...the lives of the trees... all we know is that it's a tree... that really taught me something...
the simple expression on his face and the kind of humanity that emanated from the man were amazing...
you know, he's the one who's right... we live like pigs!
you know, in speaking to him, i honestly and truly felt that class barriers are beginning to disappear
BRETÉCHER

# Mother-In-Law Blues

# a little learning

# POLITICIZED

# DIVORCE

BRETÉCHER

# TAKING THE MICKEY

BRETECHER

# SUSIE HOMEMAKER

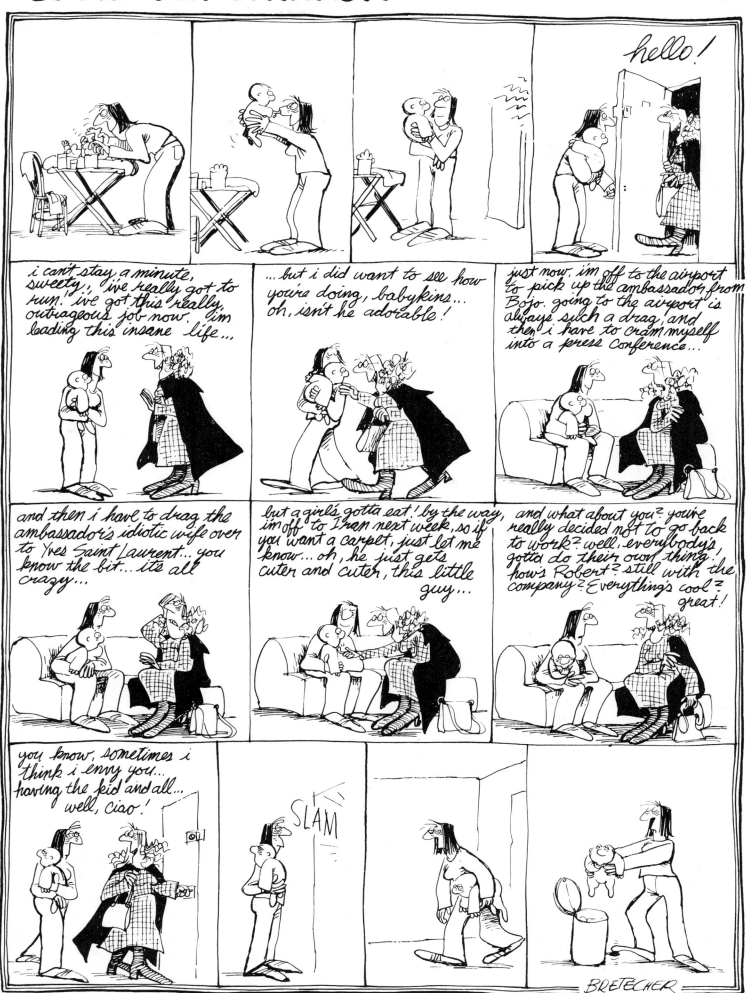

# UPLIFTING NEWS

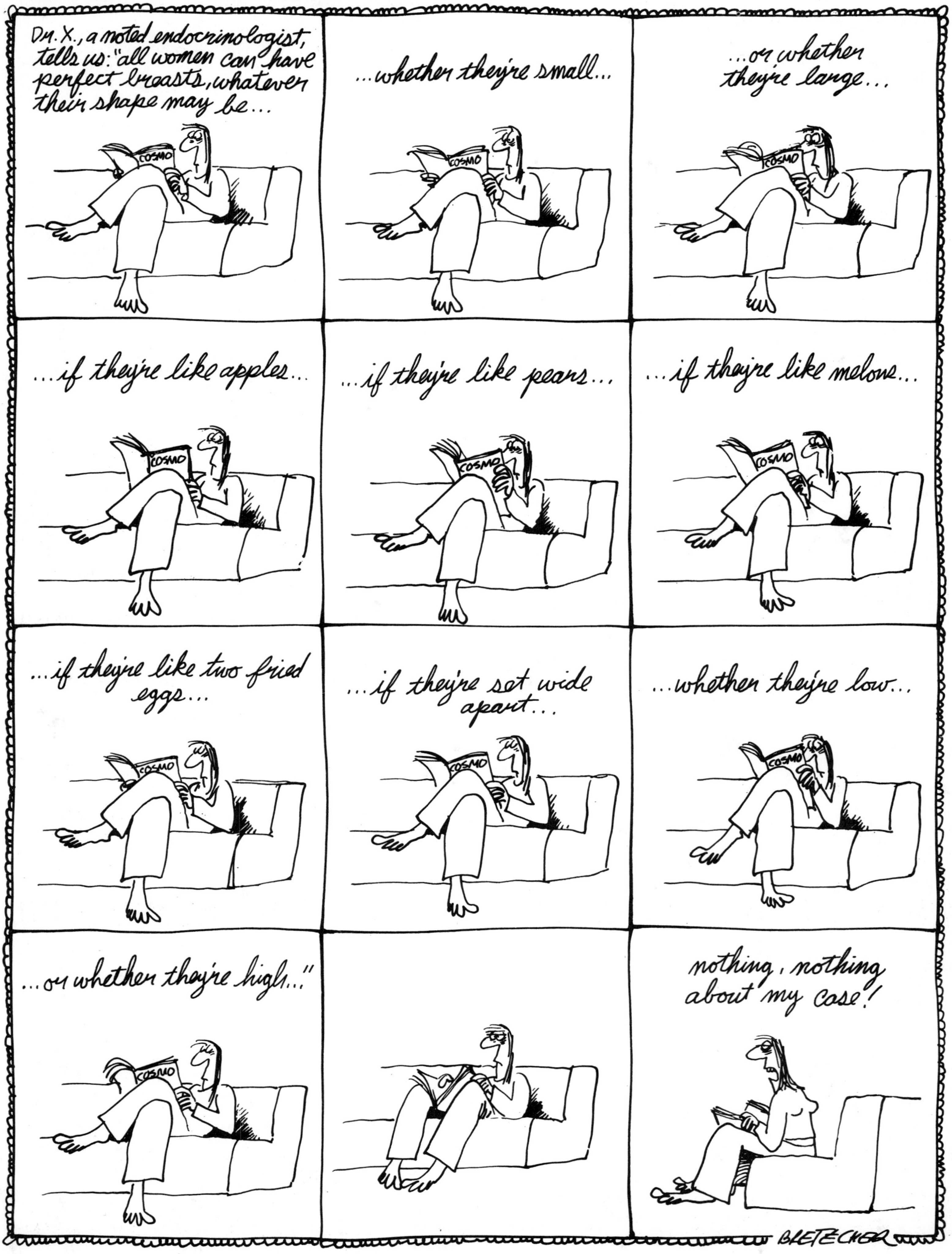

# CULTURAL BREAKTHROUGH

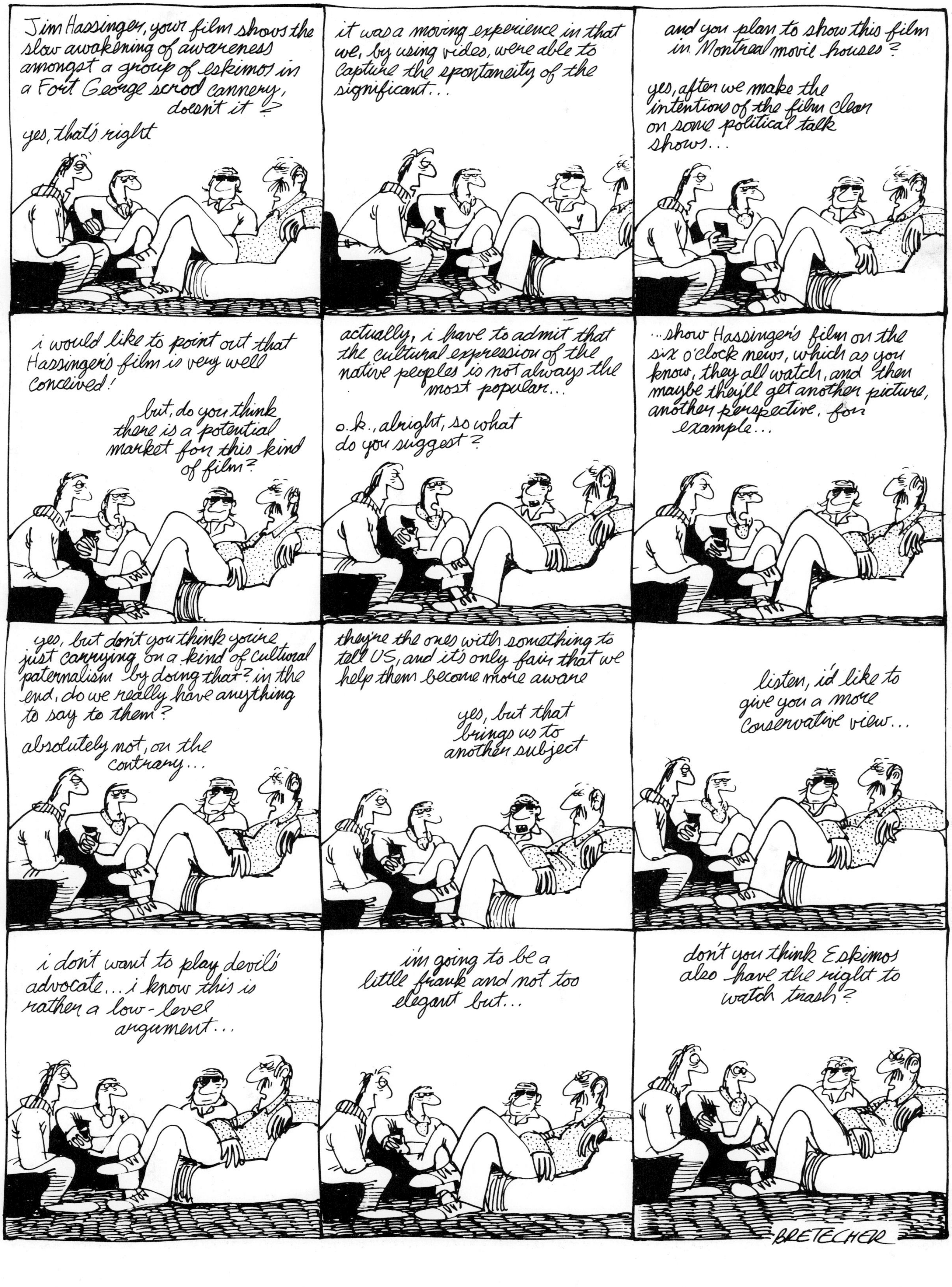

# sun worshippers

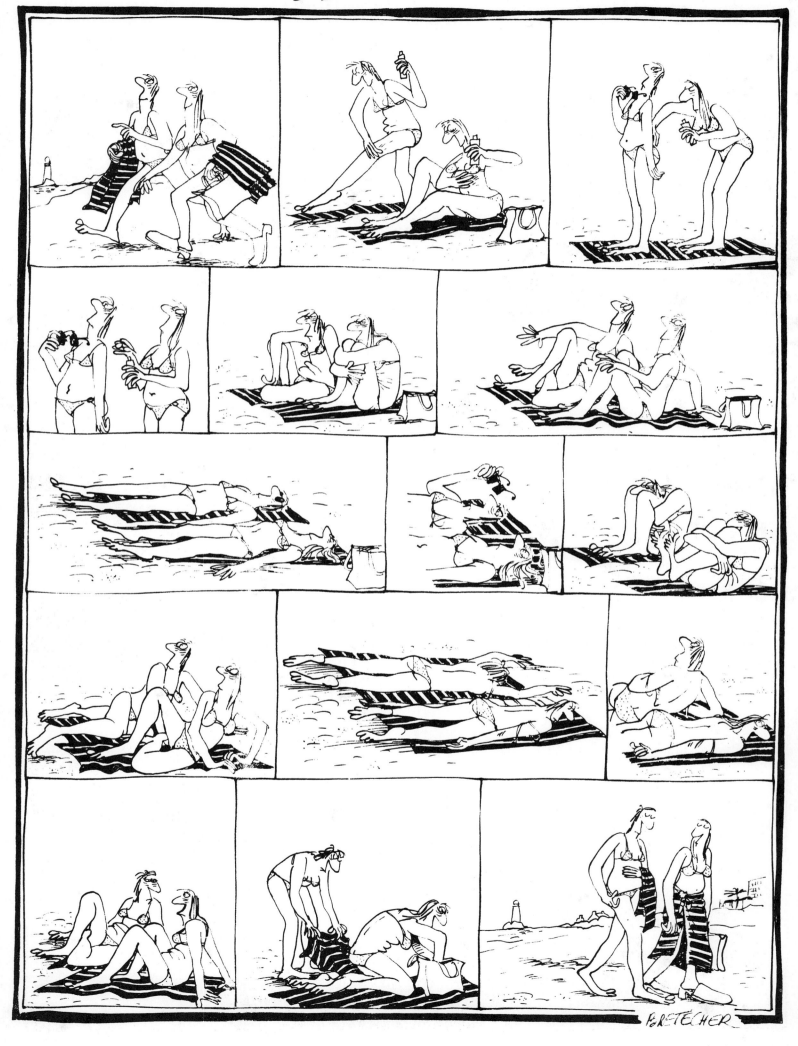

BRETECHER

# eye for an eye

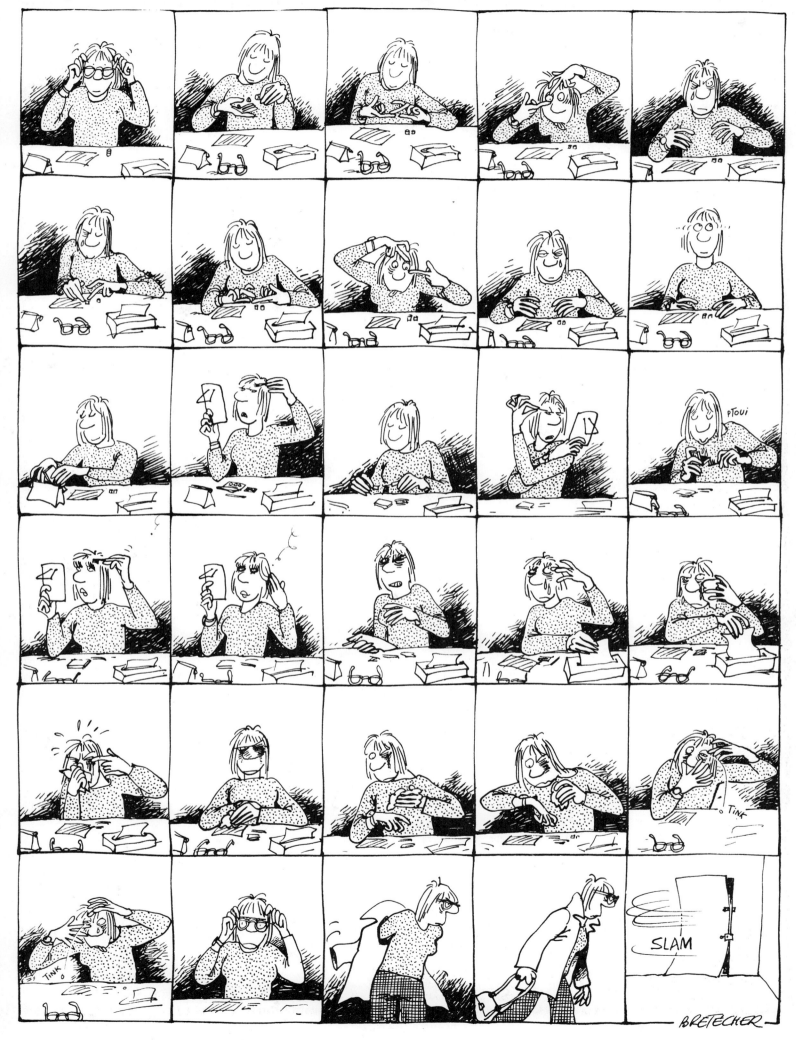

# The Secret of Happiness

# AMAZON...

# behind every great man

# FREE SPIRITS

# MOMMY

you know, in the end, Candy and Elyse got married after all...

who were the lucky guys?

just another two who've ended up trapped! but what's it all about?... gotta be a masochist!...

well, what about you, then?

well, what about you?

i know, i know!

i mean, it's better this way... i don't know... because of taxes... for the kids...

sure, i know...

let me tell you: i only got married because of my mother...

really, you, too?

you understand, she couldn't stand seeing me living in obvious sin... it made her hysterical...

just like mine...

and, of course, it had to be in a church... she would have had a heart attack if it had been a civil ceremony!

mine would have died!

they played Mendelssohn! perfect middle-class taste!

we had Schubert's "Ave Maria"!

it just wasn't worth offending the family over something like that!

how right you are!

well, are you going to baptize your kid?

certainly not! are you kidding? i figure i've made enough concessions!

but come to think of it, mummy is going to be sick about it!

BRETECHER

# Nevermore

# SATURDAY NIGHT DEAD

# THOSE HOUSEWIFE BLUES

i didn't use to care much but these days i'm beginning to understand the feminist position

just because i don't have a job and i'm not the one who brings home the bacon, i end up being the maid around here!

Stevie's from a middle-class family, so everything's got to be spic and span around the old homestead... so that i spend my days working like a dog...

you can't imagine what it's like with meals: Stevie's got to have an appetizer, a main course, and some elaborate dessert... otherwise it wouldn't be the real thing!

i'm telling you, when i see myself in the morning, standing in line with my little basket at the butcher, with all the housewife types, i say to myself: this can't be true! it's a bad dream!

i admit i'm not productive right now so this is what i've got to do, o.k., but i can assure you, it's far from fulfilling...

granted, it's also work taking care of a shop, and the customers aren't always charming, but at least you're outside the house— you get to see people!

what's more, Stevie's incredibly moody, and i have to seem interested in each and every spiritual change...

i'm telling you, i don't have any space of my own where i can have a little peace when i want it...

i don't know how people do it... i really think it's hell to be a couple!

there's Stevie now!

hi, what's for dinner?

BRETECHER

# NIGHT ON THE TOWN

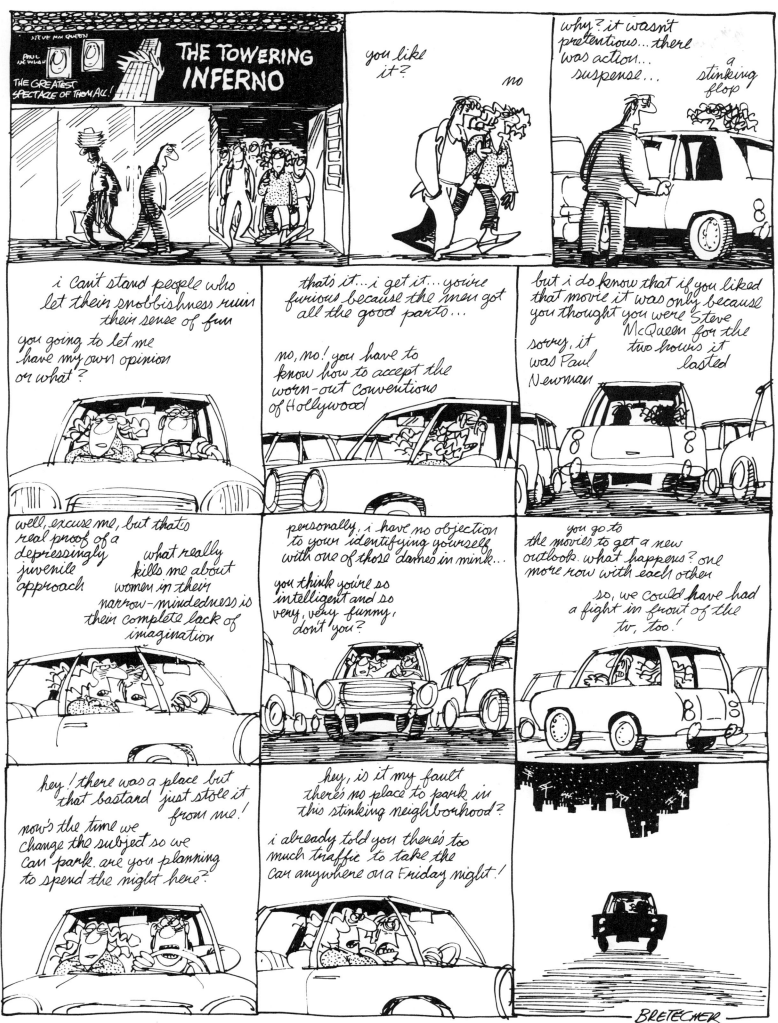

# Susan Devins

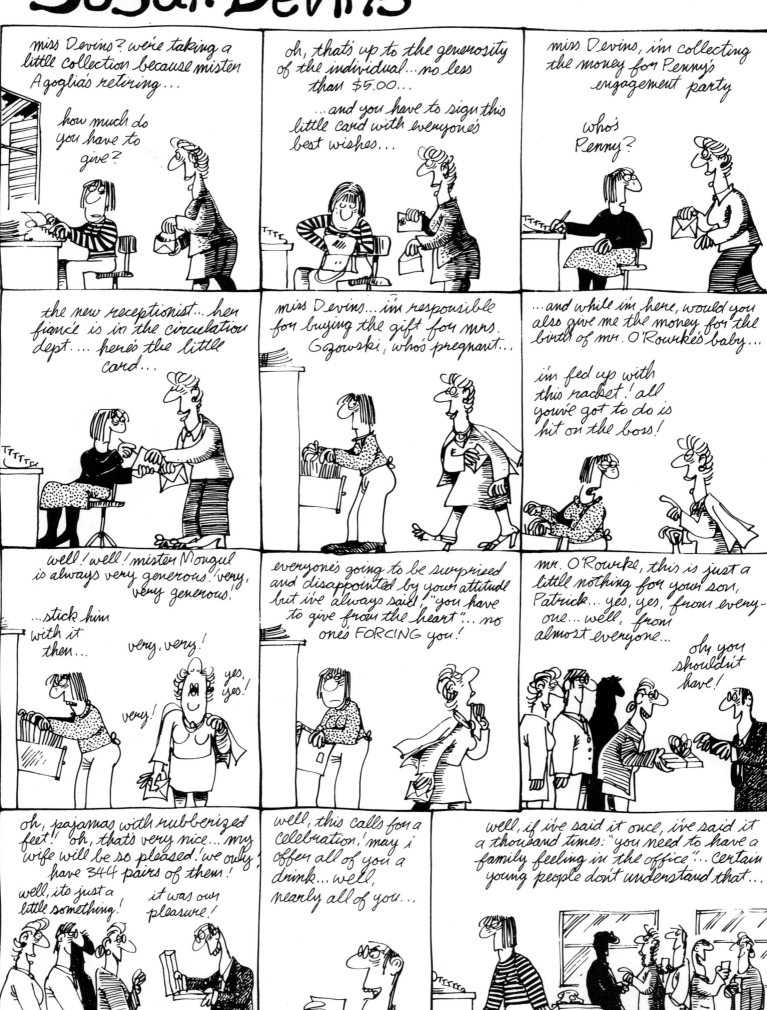

# Kathy

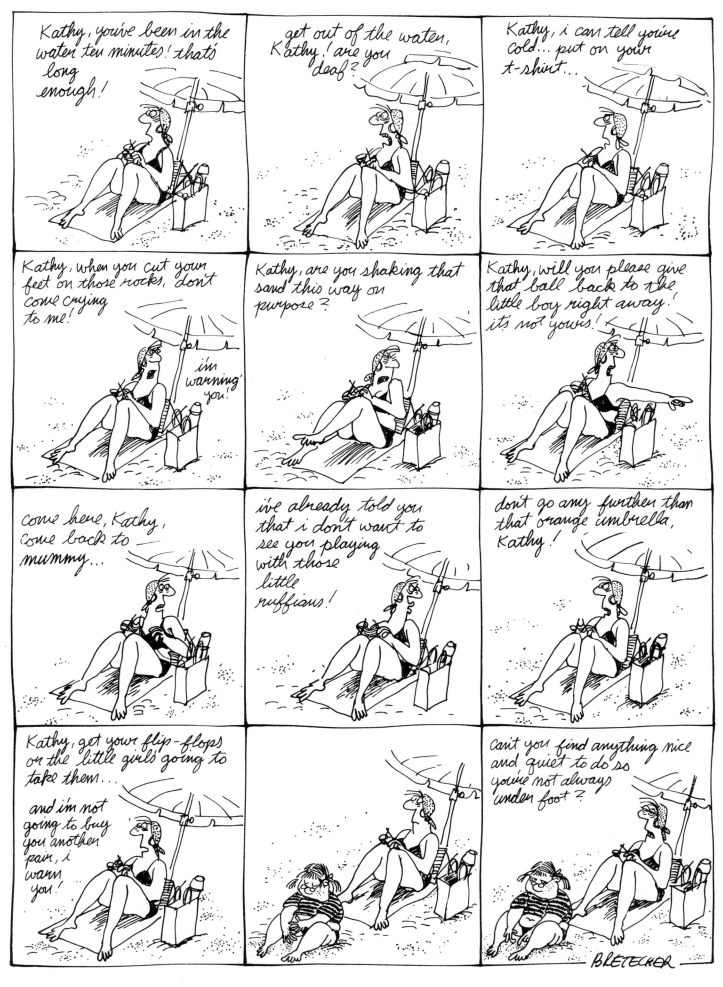

# COUNTERCULTURE

# A MAID OF CONSTANT SORROW

so he said to me: "do you think i'm going out with you so we can talk about the condition of your soul? when are we going to sleep together?"

that bugged me, so i said to him: "listen, i'm bugged because right now just isn't the right time..."

so he said to me, "terrific! we really need an argument like this. if i go out with you, it's not for your mind, you know, so when are we going to make it?"

so i said to him, "listen, you're bugging me because i'm into being faithful right now..."

so he said to me, "ho, ha, ha! all you liberated women are the same, you make me sick! when it's a question of talking, that's fine!... you're even more screwed up than your grand-mothers..."

"...'pure as the driven snow'? isn't that a bit outdated? you didn't learn that at the women's conference, did you?"

so, i didn't know what to say to him then, so i said: "anyway, i'm frigid."

so he said to me: "hey, that's what they all say, when it gets to this point. it must be some kind of defense mechanism, the last stand. anyway, if it's true..."

...that's just because you've been badly balled, you poor kid! you want to go on like that for your whole life?...

maybe you should think about taking advantage of the demand while it's there, 'cause by the time you're 56, it'll be all over."

you understand, he didn't turn me on, i can't stand him really, but i couldn't say that to him... it wouldn't be nice...

and anyway, he wouldn't believe me!

BRETÉCHER

# THE CONQUISTADORS

# AIRPORT '78

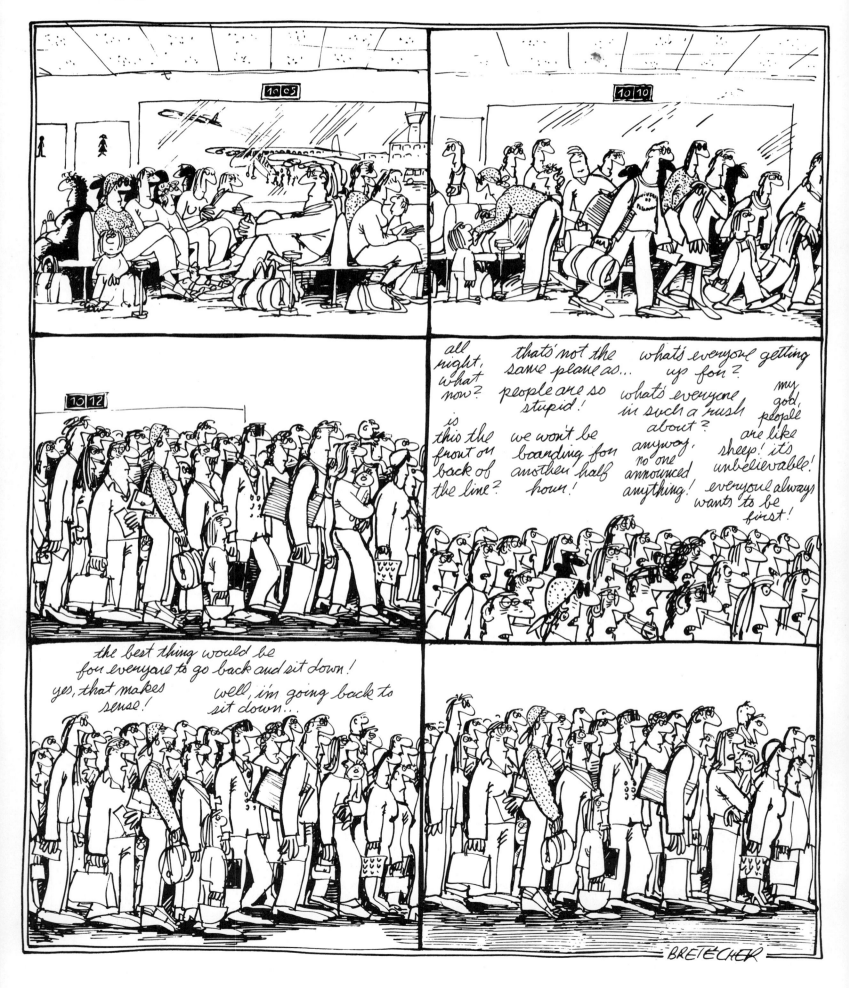

# THE WALKING WOUNDED

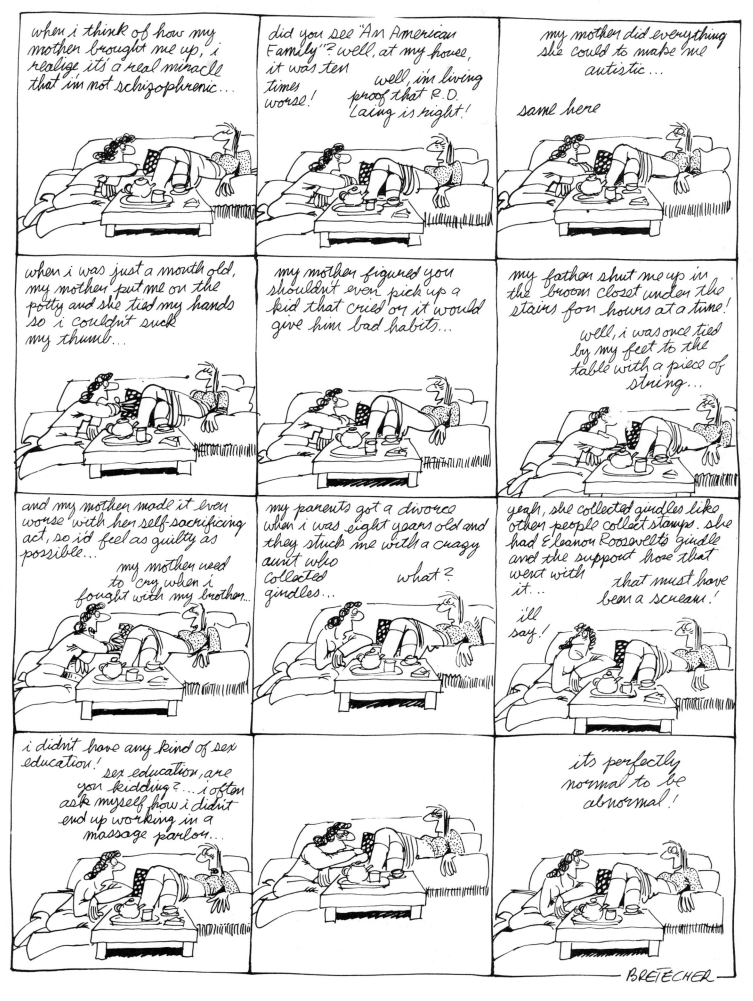

# A MAN OF SIMPLE TASTES

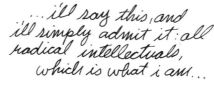
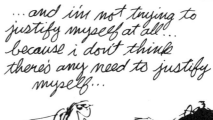

honesty is crucial in this discussion, so i'm going to be honest...

...i'll say this, and i'll simply admit it: all radical intellectuals, which is what i am...

...and i'm not trying to justify myself at all... because i don't think there's any need to justify myself...

...i want to say it and i won't hesitate to say it, because it's true, and valid...

...i should explain my concept of integrity again, but that would take us off the subject...

...i want to say that at the level of dis-trac-tion...

...i know i could pretend that what i'm trying to do is integrate the cultural demands of the majority of Americans, and that wouldn't be entirely untrue...

...but i don't want to hide behind that easy argument...

...i simply want to say that from time to time, and i say "from time to time" because there's no need to exaggerate anything...

...it's actually only when i'm really exhausted, when i've had a particularly trying day...

...and i'm not afraid to say it.... i'll simply admit it.... because it seems significant to me...

...but in the evenings, i sit and watch the idiocy that's on tv!

BRETECHER

# MOTHER HENS

# RAD LIB

things are getting sort of out of hand with the girls... i'd like to drop it

when we organized the women's group, we thought we could initiate some action at another level...

so we organized consciousness-raising meetings where girls could express themselves, and you know, it's been three years, and all they've talked about is sex, sex, sex!

after all the abortion stories i've heard, all i want to do is have six kids...

they say that i refuse to face my problems out of fear of questioning my whole self. good, agreed, o.k., if you insist...

only if i mention i need money to buy a new hair dryer, they tell me i'm falling into masculine traps

it's making me nervous

i'm starting to get tired of the theories... and i find that for myself, the total elimination of guys from the surface of the globe is just a little too theoretical...

shit

so now they're calling me a heterosexual!

BRETÉCHER

# the working class

# CELEBRITIES

# PIONEERS

over at "New Times," we've fought hard, and we've fought them all...

we've fought against the Angolan incursion...

we've violently attacked both anti-Semitism and Zionism

we've fought for the whales and the porpoises, and we've defended the right to abortion on demand

we've taken a stand against the anti-bussing forces...and the misrepresentation of the homosexuals in the media...

we opened the case against the CIA and took the consequences...

we've battled against the American Medical Association and the big brand name drug labs...

so while we welcome precise criticism, no one could accuse us of not being aggressive!

Jason, honey, go play somewhere else. i'm starting to get damn mad!

BRETÉCHER

# intellectuals

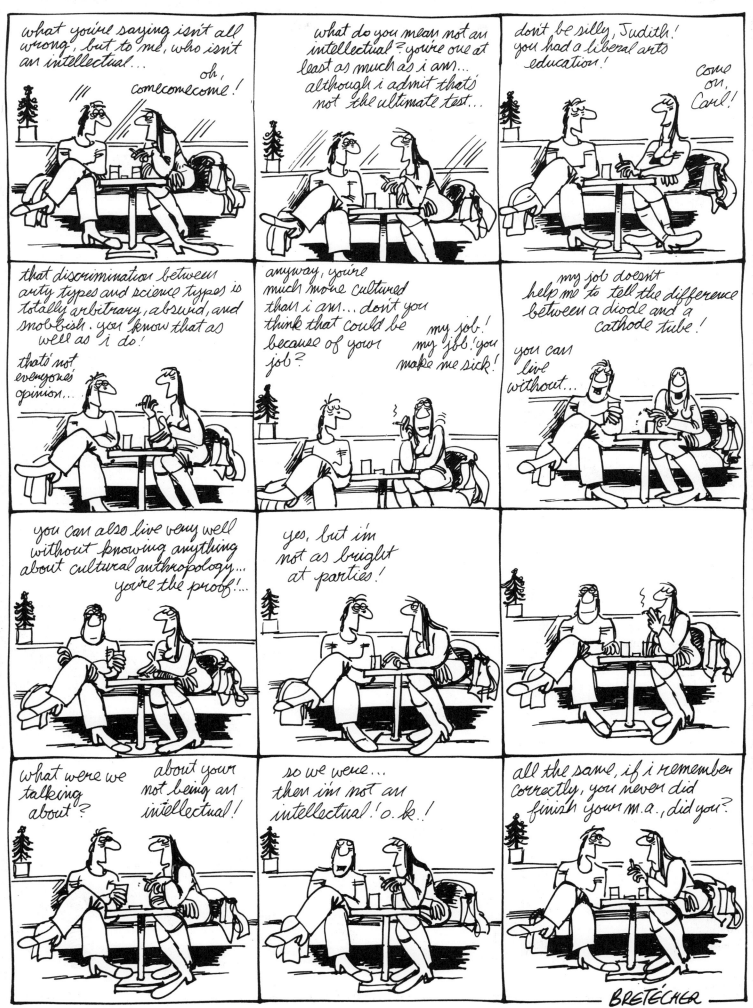

# A LIFE IN THE THEATER

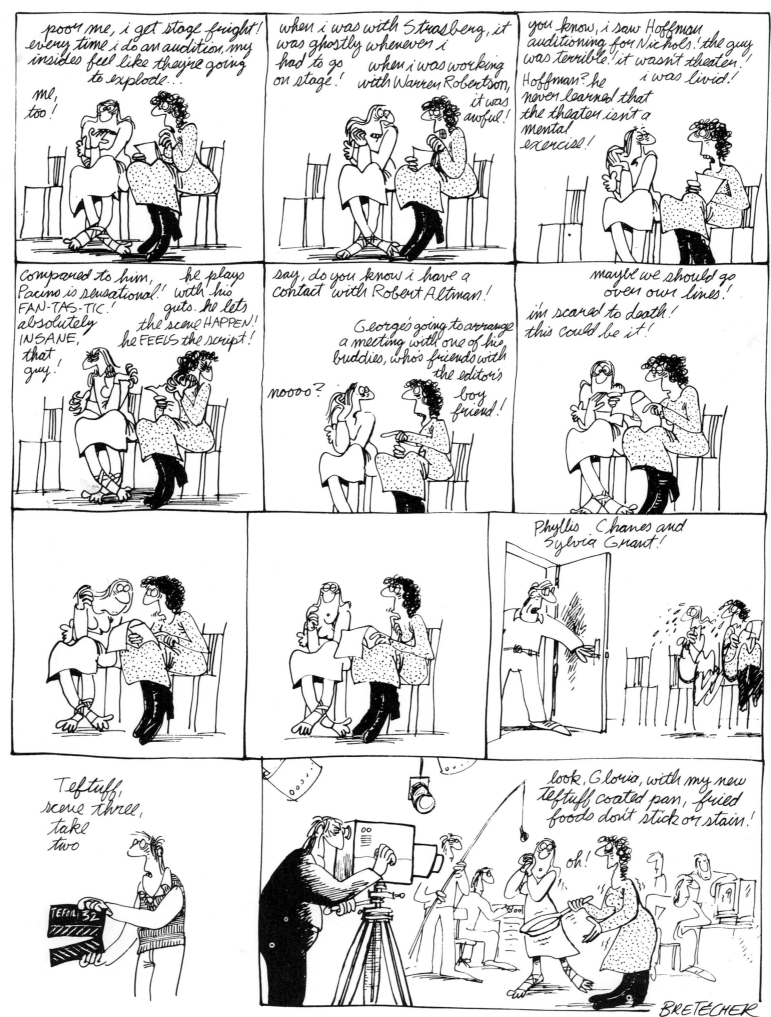

BRETECHER

# young and foolish

# The DEBATE

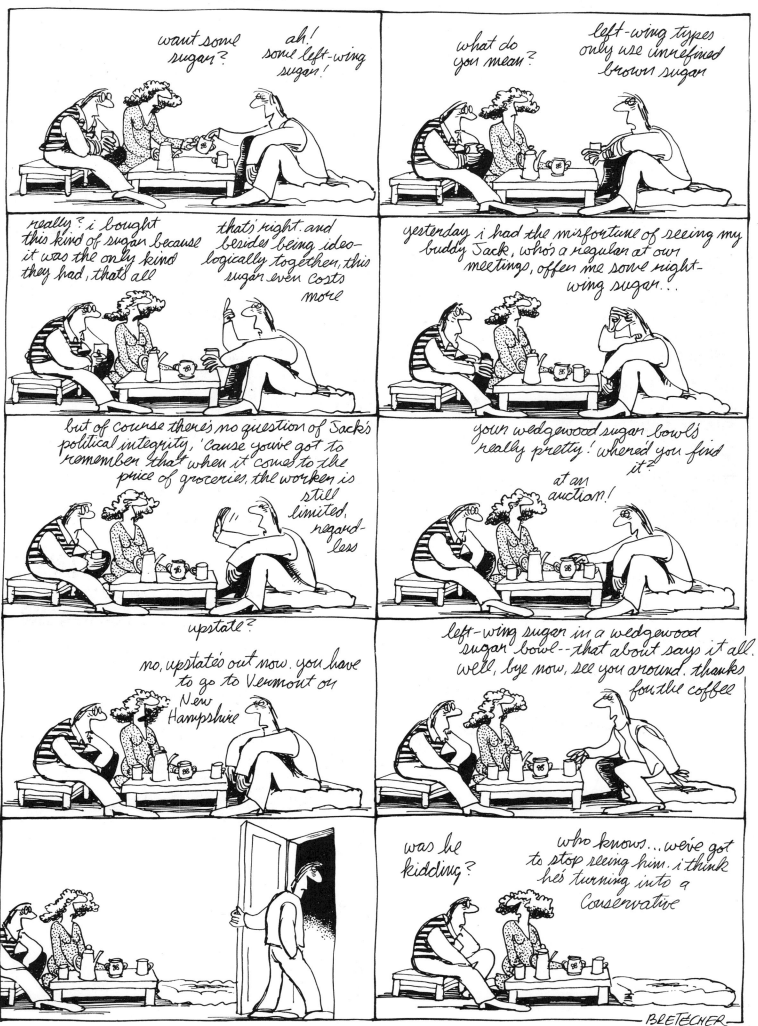

**Other** *National Lampoon* **books:**

*French Comics (The Kind Men Like)*
*Sunday Newspaper Parody*
*Animal House*